Longman Test Practice Kits

English

Key Stage 1

Alan Gardiner

LONGMAN

LONGMAN TEST PRACTICE KITS

Series editors
Geoff Black and Stuart Wall

Titles available

Key Stage 1	*Key Stage 2*	*Key Stage 3*
English	English	English
Mathematics	Mathematics	Mathematics
Mental Maths Test	Mental Maths Test	Mental Maths Test
	Science	Science

Addison Wesley Longman Limited
Edinburgh Gate, Harlow
Essex CM20 2JE, England
and Associated Companies throughout the world

© Addison Wesley Longman 1999

The right of Alan Gardiner to be identified as author of this work has been asserted by him in accordance with the Copyright, Designs and Patents Act 1988

First published 1999

British Library Cataloguing in Publication Data
A catalogue entry for this title is available from the British Library

ISBN 0-582-41489-X

Set by 32 in Futura, Frutiger Light and Bauer Bodini
Printed in Great Britain by Henry Ling Limited, at the Dorset Press, Dorchester, Dorset

Table of contents

Acknowledgements

The author and publishers are grateful to the following for permission to reproduce text and illustrations:

- **David Higham Associates** for *Bhalloo the Greedy Bear* by Pratima Mitchell; © Pratima Mitchell 1999. Originally published in *Our Favourite Stories from Around the World*, part of 'The Longman Book Project' published by Addison Wesley Longman Ltd.

- **Ladybird Books Ltd** for *Time for School*, written by Marie Birkinshaw with illustrations by Tony Kenyon, from *The Ghost House*, part of the 'Read with Ladybird' series published by Ladybird Books Ltd.

The Key Stage 1 National Tests

English at Key Stage 1

- During the last year in infant school (Year 2), most children take Key Stage 1 National Assessment Tests in English and Mathematics.
- The National Curriculum for English is divided into three parts, known as Attainment Targets:
    - AT1   Speaking and Listening
    - AT2   Reading
    - AT3   Writing, including handwriting and spelling

    The National Tests assess aspects of Attainment Targets 2 and 3.
- These National Tests (sometimes called SATs) take place in May of Year 2. Children take the tests in their own schools, and the tests are marked by their own teachers.
- There are two types of test in English:

    The Reading Comprehension Test   Here your child is asked to read independently some passages of fiction and non-fiction, and to answer some questions on these passages. The questions are intended to test how well your child has understood what he or she has read. There are two tests, one at Level 2 and one at Level 3. The Level 3 test is more difficult and is only taken by a minority of pupils.

    The Spelling Test   This assesses how accurately your child can spell a range of simple and more difficult words.
- When you receive the results of your child's National Test, you will also receive a teacher assessment of your child's ability, based on a close monitoring of your child's progress during the year. In addition to the National Tests, teachers also use separate reading and writing tasks to assess the ability of pupils.
- The results of both the National Tests and the teacher assessments are expressed as *levels* of achievement. This grading system is explained below.

Levels of achievement

Achievement in English is divided into Levels 1–4 at Key Stage 1. You can see from the table below that your child is expected to reach Level 2 by the end of Key Stage 1.

Level	Achievement
4	Exceptional performance
3	Exceeded targets for age group
2	Achieved targets for age group
1	Working towards targets for age group

A typical 7 year old would therefore be at Level 2. The main Key Stage 1 Tests cover work up to Level 3, though there are also special arrangements for the most able 7 year old pupils to be assessed at Level 4 and above.

Using this book

This section of the book discusses the tests and includes advice on how to carry them out. The rest of the book includes the following:

- **Level 2 Reading Comprehension Test**
- **Level 3 Reading Comprehension Test**
- **Spelling Test**
- **Answers**   Answers to the test questions, and guidance on awarding marks
- **Marking Scheme**   How to calculate the overall grade or Level of your child's result.

Examiner's tips provide helpful advice from the examiner to help improve your child's marks.

Which practice tests should my child take?

Your child's teacher will decide whether your child should take a Level 2 or Level 3 Reading Comprehension Test (some children take both). The Level 3 test is more difficult and only a minority of children take it. If you are not sure which test your child will be taking, start with the Level 2 test. After you have marked the test, refer to the Marking Scheme on page 59. If your child has not scored a mark in the Level 2A range (24–29), he or she is probably not yet ready for the Level 3 test. Don't be worried by this – remember the typical 7 year old is working at Level 2, and your child has plenty of time to improve! If your child *has* achieved a mark in the Level 2A range, he or she is probably in a good position to attempt the Level 3 test.

The Spelling Test is more straightforward, as all children who sit the National Tests in English take the same Spelling Test. The practice test in this book is similar to the test that is set at Key Stage 1.

Taking the practice tests

Specific information on carrying out the different tests is given before each one. Here though are some important general points.

- Choose a place where your child will be comfortable and able to concentrate.
- Your child will need a pencil or pen and an eraser. If an eraser is not used, tell your child to cross out neatly anything he or she wishes to change or correct. No paper is needed, as answers can be written in the spaces provided.
- Do not ask your child to do all the tests at once. In particular, each Reading Comprehension Test is in two parts and your child should take a break between them.
- The detailed information accompanying the tests explains the amount of help you can give your child at the beginning of each one. Try to be encouraging and supportive, and try to make the tests an enjoyable experience for your child. For more ways to help your child perform well in the tests, see the *Examiner's tips* below, and at the beginning of Part 1 (the Reading Comprehension Tests) and Part 2 (the Spelling Test).

Examiner's tips

- Use this book to familiarise your child with the likely format of the National Tests, so that he or she is confident about what to expect.
- Use the results of the practice tests to highlight where your child needs extra help or practice.
- Be positive towards your child, offering encouragement and support. Give praise for making an effort as well as for getting the right answers. Try not to be critical, as this can make a child disheartened.
- Take an interest in your child's work. Talk to your child about the practice tests, and about the work he or she does in school.
- Talk to your child's teacher about the work being done in school, and about ways you can build on this work at home.
- Try to make sure your child is relaxed when the time for the National Tests arrives. If you can make the practice tests in this book an enjoyable experience for your child, he or she is more likely to enjoy the real tests. It may help both you and your child to be less anxious if you remember that the National Tests are not the only assessment made of your child's progress (see page v).

PART 1

Reading Comprehension Tests

Examiner's tips

- Encourage your child to keep looking back at the passages when answering the questions. This makes incorrect answers much less likely.

- Make sure your child understands that the questions usually relate to specific parts of the passages. In the Level 2 test, the questions are on the same page as the part of the passage they refer to. In the Level 3 test, there are page numbers in brackets telling your child which part of the passage he or she needs to look at.

- With multiple choice questions, encourage your child to think about all of the possible answers (usually there are four). Sometimes children rush these questions and tick the first or second option without considering the other two.

- Encourage your child to read, and take an interest in your child's reading. Read stories with your child, and encourage your child to read independently as well. You can improve your child's comprehension skills by talking about stories – how does your child feel about particular characters, for example, or about the way a story ends?

- Encourage your child to read other kinds of writing as well. Help your child to understand that books can contain information as well as stories.

Reading Comprehension Test

How to conduct the test

This test is in two parts: a story, *Time for School* (pages 7–14), and a set of passages under the general heading *Time* (pages 15–20). The questions in each part test your child's understanding of what he or she has read.

There is no time limit for completing the test, but your child is unlikely to need more than about 45 minutes overall. You should encourage your child to take a break between the two parts of the test.

You should also encourage your child to attempt all the questions in the test. If children are unsure of an answer, it is better to make the best guess they can than to write nothing at all. If you notice that your child is stuck on a question, you could suggest moving on to the next question and returning to the other one later.

The answers requiring a written response do not need to be complete sentences. In this test children are also not penalised for poor handwriting, punctuation or spelling, though it is sensible to encourage them to be as neat and accurate as they can. If they make a mistake, they should rub out what they have written with an eraser or cross it out neatly.

The design of the test enables you to give some help to your child in the early stages (in the National Test your child's teacher will do this). The help you should give is explained below.

Beginning the test

Before beginning the test, show your child the different sections it contains. Explain that there is a story, *Time for School*, and a set of shorter passages about *Time*.

You can read the first page of the story aloud to your child. Then talk about the first practice question, Question A. Look at the four possible answers and discuss with your child why each option is right or wrong. When you are sure your child understands why the correct answer is 'so they wouldn't be late for school', ask him or her to put a tick in the box beside this option.

Now talk to your child about Question B. This is a different kind of question, one requiring a written response. Ask your child to try to write an answer without your help. The correct answer is something like 'She closed the door'. Again, make sure your child understands why this is the right answer. Explain that there are other ways of writing the answer that would also be correct – for example 'She shut the door' or 'Mum closed the door'.

You should now ask your child to read the rest of the story independently and answer the questions without your help. Explain that there are two sorts of questions, some like Question A and some like Question B. Make sure your child understands that only one box must be ticked when answering multiple-choice questions. Encourage your child to look back at the story as often as he or she needs to help with the answers.

You can prepare your child for the second part of the test (*Time*) in exactly the same way. There are again two practice questions for you to discuss with your child before he or she tackles the rest independently.

Out and About

Name	
Score	Level and grade

Time for School
written by Marie Birkinshaw
illustrated by Tony Kenyon

"Hurry up," said Mum, "or we'll be late for school."

We all rushed downstairs, picked up our bags and went outside. Mum closed the door.

A Why did Mum tell everyone to hurry up?

☐ she was going to work

☐ so they wouldn't be late for school

☐ the children were still in bed

☐ someone was at the door

B What did Mum do when everyone was outside?

....

"No, wait!" said Kate.

"I've forgotten my homework. Mrs James will go mad if I don't have it with me this time!"

So we all went back inside

---

1 What did Kate forget?

....

2 What will happen if Kate does not take her work to school?

☐ they will all be late ☐ she will do it again

☐ Mrs James will be mad ☐ Mrs James will be pleased

8

"Be quick, Kate," cried Mum, "or we'll be very late for school, and Mrs James really will be cross with you."

Kate found her homework and rushed downstairs.
We all picked up our bags and went outside.
Mum closed the door and turned the key in the lock.
We all headed for the car.

---

3 Where was Kate's homework?

☐ upstairs   ☐ downstairs

☐ in the car   ☐ outside

4 What did the children take with them when they left the house?

....

"No, wait!" said Charlie.
"I've forgotten my sports kit and it's football today."
So we all went back inside.

"Hurry up, Charlie!" cried Mum. "We'll be late for school!"
Charlie got his sports kit and rushed downstairs.

We all picked up our bags and went outside.

5 Why did Charlie need his sports kit?

....

6 Charlie **rushed** downstairs. This means he

☐ fell   ☐ jumped

☐ ran quickly   ☐ walked slowly

Mum closed the door and turned the key in the lock. She unlocked the car and we all tried to get in the front seat. We could tell by the look on Mum's face that this was not a good idea, so we got in the back and put on our seatbelts.

---

7 Where did the children try to sit at first?

....

8 When they did this, Mum looked

☐ happy   ☐ pleased

☐ cross   ☐ sad

"I don't believe it!" cried Mum. "I've forgotten my bag! We'll never get to school at this rate."

She took off her seatbelt and went back in the house.

Mum found her bag and rushed out of the front door.

9 Why did Mum have to go back in the house?

....

10 What did Mum do before she got out of the car?

....

She locked the door, got back into the car, put on her seatbelt and started the car up.

"Can we have the radio on, please, Mum?" said Kate.

"OK," said Mum. "But let's get going or we'll never get to school today."

---

11 Mum put the radio on because

[ ] she wanted to know the time

[ ] Charlie asked her to

[ ] Kate asked her to

[ ] she wanted to hear some music

12 Mum says "**let's get going**" because

[ ] she likes to listen to the radio

[ ] she is in a hurry

[ ] the car won't start

[ ] the radio won't work

And the man on the radio said, "Good morning! Now for the latest news on this lovely Saturday morning . . ."

WHOOPEE!

Mum cried, "Saturday? I don't believe it!"

Kate and Charlie cried, "WHOOPEE!"

---

13 Who tells them it is Saturday?

....

14 Do you think the children were happy or sad?

☐ happy   ☐ sad

Why do you think this?

....

....

Time

You have just read *Time for School*, a funny story about a family who made a mistake about what day of the week it was. In the next few pages you will read some more about time.

Time is very important in our lives.

- There are different times of the day – morning, afternoon, evening and night. We also divide the day up into hours and minutes.

- There are different days of the week – Sunday, Monday, Tuesday and so on.

- There are different months of the year, such as January and February. We also divide the year into seasons – spring, summer, autumn and winter.

A Hours and minutes are used to divide up

☐ days   ☐ months

☐ weeks   ☐ years

B Write down the two months of the year that are named in the passage.

....

Emily's diary

Some people write a list of the things they have to do on different days in a book called a **diary**. They do this to make sure they don't forget anything.

You can also write things down in diaries after they have happened. Some people like to do this so that a long time later they can read their diaries and remember what happened to them.

Emily is seven years old. Here is her diary for one weekend.

	SATURDAY		SUNDAY
Morning	Tidy bedroom	**Morning**	Go swimming
Afternoon	Shopping with Mum	**Afternoon**	Sally's birthday party
Evening	See Gran	**Evening**	Do homework

15 What do people write in diaries?

☐ things they have forgotten   ☐ things they do not need to do

☐ things they have to do   ☐ things they want to forget

16 Why do some people like to read their old diaries?

....

17 When is Emily going to tidy her bedroom?

☐ Saturday afternoon   ☐ Saturday morning

☐ Sunday morning   ☐ Saturday evening

18 Write down **two** things that Emily is going to do on Sunday.

....

Clocks

We use clocks to tell us the time.
Clocks tell us when it is time to get up in the morning,
when to go to school and when to go to bed at night.

People have not
always had clocks.
Thousands of
years ago people
used the sun to tell
what time of day it
was.

Another old way of
telling the time
used water. Large
bowls were filled
with water. As time
passed, the water
slowly trickled out.

---

19 Did people first use the sun to tell the time **before**
they had clocks or **after** they had clocks?

....

20 When people used water to tell the time, what was the
water put in?

....

21 Using the sun and using water are both

☐ new ways of telling
the time

☐ ways of telling what
year it is

☐ old ways of telling
the time

☐ ways of telling if it is
light or dark

Seasons

Each year has twelve months and four seasons. The seasons are spring, summer, autumn and winter. Here are some things that happen in the different seasons.

- In **spring** many plants grow more quickly and we see more flowers.
- In **summer** the days are longer and it gets dark later.
- In **autumn** leaves fall from the trees.
- In **winter** the weather is colder and it gets dark earlier.

---

22 How many seasons are there?

☐ Twelve ☐ Twenty four

☐ Three ☐ Four

23 Write down **two** things that happen in summer.

....

24 When do leaves fall from the trees?

....

19

Land of the Midnight Sun

The seasons are different in different parts of the world.

At the north pole, which is at the top of the world, there is a time during the summer when it never becomes dark. The sun carries on shining all day and all night. This part of the world is called the Land of the Midnight Sun.

Later in the year, when it is winter, the sun never shines and it stays dark all through the day.

---

25 Where in the world is the north pole?

....

26 The Land of the Midnight Sun is called this because

☐ it is always dark   ☐ it is always midnight

☐ the sun sometimes shines at midnight   ☐ the sun never shines

27 In the Land of the Midnight Sun, it stays dark all day in

☐ spring   ☐ autumn

☐ summer   ☐ winter

Reading Comprehension Test

How to conduct the test

The test is in two parts: a story, *Bhalloo the Greedy Bear* (pages 25–30), and a set of passages under the general heading *Animal Neighbours* (pages 31–34). The questions on each part that follow test your child's understanding of what he or she has read.

There is no time limit for completing the test, but your child is unlikely to need more than about 45 minutes overall. You should encourage your child to take a break between the two parts of the test.

You should also encourage your child to attempt all the questions in the test. If children are unsure of an answer, it is better to make the best guess they can than to write nothing at all. If you notice that your child is stuck on a question, you could suggest moving on to the next question and returning to the other one later.

The answers requiring a written response do not need to be complete sentences. In this test children are also not penalised for poor handwriting, punctuation or spelling, though it is sensible to encourage them to be as neat and accurate as they can. If they make a mistake, they should rub out what they have written with an eraser or cross it out neatly.

The design of the test enables you to give some help to your child in the early stages (in the National Test your child's teacher will do this). The help you should give is explained below.

Beginning the test

Before beginning the test, show your child the different sections it contains. Explain that there is a story, *Bhalloo the Greedy Bear*, and a set of shorter passages about *Animal Neighbours*.

You can read the first page of the story aloud to your child. Then read out the first practice question, Question A. Point out the page numbers '(pages 25 and 26)' in brackets on the right-hand side of the page, above the questions. Explain that this means that looking at pages 25 and 26 will help to answer Questions A and B. Ask your child to think about the answer to Question A and to put a tick in one of the boxes. Discuss the four possible answers with your child and make sure he or she understands why the correct answer is 'at the edge of the forest'.

Now talk to your child about Question B. This is a different kind of question, one requiring a written response. Ask your child to write an answer in the space provided. The correct answer is something like 'He had eaten all the fruit in the forest near his home'. Again, make sure your child understands why this is the right answer. Explain that there are other ways of writing the answer that would also be correct – for example, 'There was no fruit left in the forest near his home'.

You should now ask your child to read the rest of the story independently and answer the questions without your help. Explain that there are two sorts of questions, some like Question A and some like Question B. Make sure your child understands that only one box must be ticked when answering multiple-choice questions, and that the page numbers in brackets above the questions show which pages to look at. Encourage your child to look back at the story as often as he or she needs to help with the answers.

When your child is ready for the second part of the test (*Animal Neighbours*), explain that the questions are of the same kind and should be answered in the same way.

In the Forest

Bhalloo
the
Greedy Bear

retold by Pratima Mitchell
illustrated by Jane Bottomley

Bhalloo, the big brown bear, was always hungry. He loved
wild berries, red apples and cherries and every so often
found himself a sticky honeycomb dripping with golden
honey. One day when he had cleared the forest near his
home of every single bit of fruit, he went hunting for more
food.

At the edge of the forest, Bhalloo heard the Woodcutter talking to his wife in their cottage garden.

"I'm so hungry I could eat a bear!" said the Woodcutter. "Please, dear wife, could you cook me some of your delicious rice pudding? I'm absolutely famished!" mention of rice pudding, Bhalloo's stomach started to rumble.

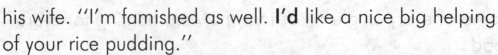

"Grr-grr" he roared, bounding up to the startled Woodcutter and his wife. "I'm famished as well. **I'd** like a nice big helping of your rice pudding."

Mrs Woodcutter thought quickly. "In that case," she said, "bring me a load of firewood from the forest and I'll get cooking straightaway." So Bhalloo lumbered off to fetch a load of firewood.

Meanwhile, the Woodcutter was feeling faint with hunger. He asked his wife to start cooking the rice pudding, which she did. She made it with milk and nuts and brown sugar and dried apricots and it smelled wonderful. Before it had time to cool, the Woodcutter grabbed the pot and ate the lot. In a few minutes, all that was left was a few grains of rice at the bottom.

27

Mrs Woodcutter was terribly frightened. She knew that Bhalloo would be angry. He might even eat them up instead! She hurried the Woodcutter to the attic and hid there with him.

Soon, they heard Bhalloo come crashing back through the forest. They heard a loud thump as he threw down the load of firewood. Then they heard his bellows of rage when he discovered the empty pot of rice pudding.

"Don't worry," Mrs Woodcutter told her trembling husband. "Bhalloo will go wild and break all our furniture, but then he'll go away and we'll be safe."

Crash, bang, smash!
Bhalloo was so furious that he flung all their kitchen pots on the floor. Then he smashed up a chair or two and then, grumbling loudly, he left. The Woodcutter and his wife sighed with relief.

Bhalloo went into the garden, hungrier than ever, and there he saw a pear tree laden with fruit. He cheered up. He grabbed a pawful of pears and devoured them. Crunch, crunch! In a minute they were gone so he grabbed some more. Crunch, crunch! He had never eaten pears before and he didn't realise that they were hard and green and unripe. He just kept on eating until there wasn't one pear left on the tree.

Poor Bhalloo! The green pears gave him a terrible tummy ache. He clutched his stomach and crawled back to his home in the forest. That was the last time that Bhalloo was so greedy and the Woodcutter and his wife were never troubled by him again. They also had a nice big bundle of firewood they could use to cook their meals.

Animal Neighbours

The story of *Bhalloo the Greedy Bear* is set in India. If you lived in a house on the edge of a forest in Britain, you would of course be very surprised if a wild bear suddenly appeared in your garden. This is because bears do not live in the wild in this country any more, although they did many hundreds of years ago.

However, many other creatures do still live happily in our gardens and forests. Some of these will be described on the next few pages.

Squirrels

Squirrels are a familiar sight in Britain, and are seen not only in woodland but also in city parks and gardens.

Most of the squirrels that live in this country are grey squirrels. Although there are now huge numbers of grey squirrels in Britain, they have only lived here for about a hundred years. At first just a few grey squirrels were brought to Britain from North America. People thought they were attractive creatures and liked the idea of squirrels living in their gardens. Since then there has been a steady increase in the numbers of grey squirrels.

The other kind of squirrel that lives in Britain is the red squirrel. The red squirrel does not come from overseas but is native to British woodlands. It is smaller than the grey squirrel, and also shyer. Grey squirrels often live close to people in cities and gardens, but red squirrels are usually only seen in the countryside. The numbers of red squirrels are falling, and they are now only found in a few parts of Britain.

Frogs

Frogs like to live in damp places and are especially likely to be seen in and around ponds.

Frogs have webbed feet, which help them to swim, and long hind legs, which are used for jumping. Their long tongues help them to catch insects. They like to eat spiders and worms.

Frogs hide away during cold weather and sleep all through the winter. They dig holes to hide in, either at the bottom of a pond or on land. When they wake up, they mate and lay eggs. They lay their eggs in jelly, called frogspawn. If you look in a pond early in the year, you will often see frogspawn floating on the surface.

These eggs slowly change shape and turn into tadpoles, with long tails and no legs. The tadpoles grow legs, lose their tails and turn into little frogs. Then the frogs crawl out of the water and begin to look for food and a place to live.

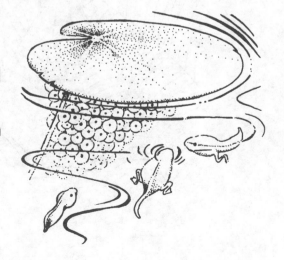

Spiders

We are all used to seeing spiders and their webs, not only outside in woods and gardens, but also sometimes inside our houses. There are many different kinds of spider. In fact there are about thirty thousand species altogether, though many of these do not live in Britain.

Most spiders have eight legs and eight eyes. They weave webs which are traps to catch the insects they need for food. The thread used to make the web comes from a special substance that the spider makes in her own body. Although this thread is very fine and thin, it is also very strong. A perfectly made spider's web is one of nature's most beautiful sights.

In the Forest

Reading Comprehension

Name	
Score	Level and grade

(pages 25 and 26)

A Where was the Woodcutter's cottage?

☐ in the middle of the forest

☐ by the sea

☐ at the edge of the forest

☐ a long way away from the forest

B Why didn't Bhalloo carry on hunting for food near his home?

....

....

Bhalloo the Greedy Bear

(pages 26 and 27)

1 Why does Bhalloo's stomach start to rumble?

....

....

2 How does Mrs Woodcutter get Bhalloo to go away?

....

....

3 When the Woodcutter eats the rice pudding it is

☐ very cold   ☐ cool

☐ hot   ☐ not cooked

(pages 28 and 29)

4 The words **rage**, **furious** and **grumbling** all show that Bhalloo was

☐ angry   ☐ sad

☐ noisy   ☐ hungry

(pages 28 and 29)

5 How can you tell that the Woodcutter was feeling frightened as he hid in the attic?

....

....

6 Why did Mrs Woodcutter tell her husband that he did not need to worry?

....

....

7 After Bhalloo saw the pear tree, he felt

☐ hungrier than ever   ☐ happier

☐ upset   ☐ angrier

8 Bhalloo ate every pear on the tree. This showed that he was

☐ clever   ☐ a slow eater

☐ greedy   ☐ curious

(pages 29 and 30)

9 Why did the pears give Bhalloo a tummy ache?

....

....

(whole story)

10 Although he did not mean to, Bhalloo had helped the Woodcutter and his wife. In what way?

....

....

11 Did you feel sorry for Bhalloo at the end of the story?

☐ Yes   ☐ No

Why?

....

....

Animal Neighbours

(page 31)

12 Why would you be surprised if a bear appeared in a garden in Britain?

....

....

(page 32)

13 In Britain, you are more likely to see a grey squirrel than a red squirrel. This is because

☐ grey squirrels are bigger

☐ there are more grey squirrels

☐ grey squirrels only live in the countryside

☐ grey squirrels only live in cities

14 Why is it surprising that there are so many grey squirrels in Britain?

....

....

15 One difference between red squirrels and grey squirrels is that

☐ red squirrels are native to Britain

☐ grey squirrels have lived in Britain longer

☐ grey squirrels are shyer

☐ red squirrels are bigger

(page 33)

16 Why are you likely to find frogs in or near ponds?

....

....

17 Frogs lay their eggs

☐ during cold weather   ☐ in the summer

☐ in the middle of winter   ☐ early in the year

18 Describe **two** differences between tadpoles and frogs.

....

....

(page 34)

19 Tick the two words that mean the same as each other.

☐ **weave** and **thread**   ☐ **fine** and **strong**

☐ **kinds** and **species**   ☐ **substance** and **web**

(page 34)

20 Why do spiders make webs?

....

....

21 The thread that is used to make a spider's web is

☐ thick and strong ☐ easy to break

☐ thin but hard to break ☐ thick and beautiful

(whole passage)

22 All of the animals that have been described

☐ are disappearing from Britain ☐ came to Britain from other countries

☐ can be seen in the countryside but not in cities ☐ can be seen in Britain

PART 2

Spelling Test

Examiner's tips

- Help your child to keep a list of words that he or she tends to spell incorrectly. Encourage your child to use these words regularly in their own writing, so as to get into the habit of spelling them correctly.
- Children can test themselves in the following way:
  Look at the word.
  Say the spelling out loud.
  Cover the word so you cannot see it.
  Write it down.
- Help your child to get used to some of the spelling patterns that commonly occur in words. Examples of these include:
  Groups of letters that occur at the **beginnings** of words (e.g. **un-**, **dis-**).
  Groups of vowels that occur in the **middle** of words (e.g. **ai**, **oa**, **ie**).
  Groups of letters that occur at the **ends** of words (e.g. **-ed**, **-ing**, **-ful**).
- Help your child to break down words into separate sounds or syllables (e.g. her-self, el-e-phant). This makes spelling, and the reading of unfamiliar words, easier.
- An understanding of rhyme helps your child to develop an awareness of sound patterns and an understanding of the link between sounds and letters. In this way, poems, songs and nursery rhymes can help with your child's spelling.

How to conduct the test

The Spelling Test is in two parts. In the first part, your child is asked to show his or her knowledge of the correct spelling of the words represented by the small pictures (on page 47) next to the main picture (on page 46). In the second part, there is a story with some words missing. You read the story aloud to your child, telling your child the words that are missing. Your child then writes these words in the spaces provided. There is no time limit for completing the test, but the whole test is unlikely to take more than about thirty minutes.

You should introduce the Spelling Test by looking at it with your child and explaining that it is in two parts. The main picture on page 46 goes with the story on pages 48 and 49 and both have the title *Market Day*.

Part 1

Show your child the small picture of a cup on page 45. Ask your child what the picture shows. When you have agreed that it shows a **cup**, ask your child to write this word in the space below the picture. When your child has done this, talk to your child about the answer and make sure he or she knows the correct spelling. This is a practice question and is not worth any marks.

Now talk to your child about the large picture and the smaller pictures next to it. Make sure your child knows what each small picture represents. *You can tell your child what each picture shows* (though try to get your child to tell you first), but obviously you should not tell your child how to spell the words. The ten words are:

coat	glass	clock	clown	bag
balloons	ball	dress	seat	train

Your child should write the words in the spaces below the pictures. If he or she has difficulty with a word, encourage your child to write the beginning of the word, followed by any other letters or sounds that they think are correct.

Part 2

A full version of the story that is used in the test appears on page 58. You will find it easier if you make a copy of this to read to your child.

Read the story aloud, asking your child to listen carefully. Then look with your child at the version of the story that appears on pages 48 and 49. Explain that this is the same story but some words are missing. Tell your child that you are going to read the story aloud again and that wherever there is a space, he or she should wait to hear you say the word then write it in the space.

The first word is for practice. Read the first sentence and check that your child understands that 'on' should be written in the first space. Then read the rest of the story, pausing at each of the words in bold print. Allow your child time to write each word. You can repeat the words if necessary. As with Part 1 of the test, if children have difficulty with a word they should be encouraged to write the beginning of the word, followed by any other letters or sounds that they think are correct.

Market Day

Spelling

Market Day – Part 1

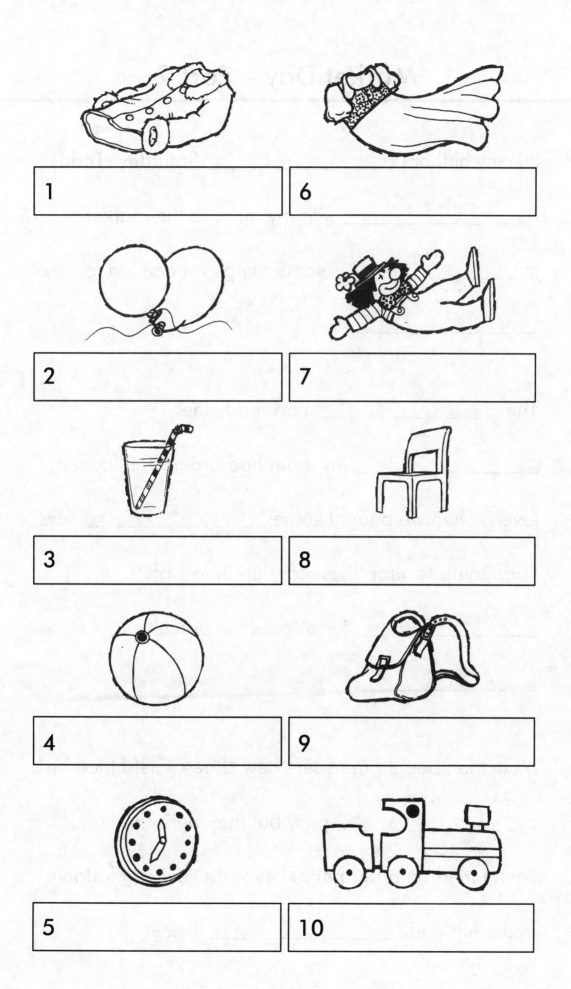

1

6

2

7

3

8

4

9

5

10

Market Day – Part 2

It is my birthday _____ Saturday. Today

I _____ with my mum to the market

to _____ some things we needed for my

_____ .

The _____ had ready the

_____ my mum had ordered. It looked

lovely. Then we bought some _____ toys.

I am going to wrap these toys up in lots of

_____ for a 'pass the parcel'

_____ .

Mum then bought me some new shoes. First I tried on

a _____ pair, but they were too tight.

Then I tried on a red pair. They were very comfortable

and Mum and I _____ these.

Mum then bought some _____. She

bought _____ and eggs from the dairy

counter. She also bought oranges and

_____ from the _____ and

_____ stall.

Then we met Grandad. He was going

to _____ us carry everything back

_____. First we all went to the café. Mum

and Grandad had some coffee and shared a

_____. I had an orange

_____ and a packet of

_____.

PART 3

Answers

Reading Comprehension Tests

- Read through the Reading Comprehension passages before marking your child's answers.
- Use the answers on the following pages to decide how many marks to award your child.
- Most questions are worth a maximum of one mark, but a few are worth two marks.
- With the multiple-choice questions, you simply need to check whether your child has ticked the correct box.
- The other questions require a short written response. Your child's answer does not need to use exactly the same words as the answer that is given. Often there are different ways of wording a correct answer. If your child has the right idea, mark the answer as correct.
- Answers do not have to be complete sentences, and you do not need to deduct any marks for poor handwriting or spelling. Remember the purpose of this test is to assess how well your child has *understood* what he or she has read. You can though encourage your child to write neatly and to take care over their handwriting, punctuation and spelling.
- When you have finished marking the answers, add up the total mark and refer to the Marking Scheme on page 59 to assess the overall grade or level of your child's result.

Level 2 Reading Comprehension Test

Use these answers to mark your child's work, after reading the general guidance on marking the Reading Comprehension Tests given on the previous page.

TIME FOR SCHOOL

Question	Answer	Mark
A	So they wouldn't be late for school	—
B	She closed the door	—
1	Her homework	1
2	Mrs James will be mad	1
3	Upstairs	1
4	Their bags	1
5	He was going to play football	1
6	Ran quickly	1
7	In the front seat	1
8	Cross	1
9	She had forgotten her bag	1
10	She took off her seatbelt	1
11	Kate asked her to	1
12	She is in a hurry	1
13	The man on the radio	1
14	Happy (*Reasons*: They say 'Whoopee!'/ They don't have to go to school/ It is Saturday)	1

TIME

Question	Answer	Mark
A	Days	—
B	January and February	—
15	Things they have to do	1
16	They like to remember what happened to them	1
17	Saturday morning	1
18	Any two of: Go swimming/Go to Sally's birthday party/Do her homework	1 or 2
19	Before	1
20	Large bowls	1
21	Old ways of telling the time	1
22	Four	1
23	The days are longer/It gets dark later	1 or 2
24	In autumn	1
25	At the top of the world	1
26	The sun sometimes shines at midnight	1
27	Winter	1

Level 2 Reading Comprehension Test

Maximum mark is **29**

Level 3 Reading Comprehension Test

Before using these answers to mark your child's work, make sure you have read the general guidance on marking the Reading Comprehension Tests on page 51.

BHALLOO THE GREEDY BEAR

Question	Answer	Mark
A	At the edge of the forest	—
B	He had eaten all the fruit in the forest near his home	—
1	He hears the Woodcutter mention rice pudding	1
2	She asks him to fetch firewood	1
3	Hot	1
4	Angry	1
5	He was trembling	1
6	She said that Bhalloo would break all their furniture and then he would go away	1
7	Happier	1
8	Greedy	1
9	*Any or all of*: They were hard/green/unripe	1
10	They had some firewood they could use to cook their meals.	1
11	*Answers may be either 'Yes' or 'No'. The mark is given for the* **reason**. *Give your child a mark if a sensible explanation for the answer is given. Reasons might include the following:* Yes He had a bad tummy ache No He was greedy/He smashed up the Woodcutter's house	1

ANIMAL NEIGHBOURS

Question	Answer	Mark
12	Bears do not live in the wild in Britain	1
13	There are more grey squirrels	1
14	They have only lived here for about a hundred years	1
15	Red squirrels are native to Britain	1
16	Frogs like to live in damp places	1
17	Early in the year	1
18	Tadpoles have long tails *or* Frogs have no tails Tadpoles have no legs *or* Frogs have legs	1 or 2
19	Kinds and species	1
20	They make webs to catch the insects they need for food	1
21	Thin but hard to break	1
22	Can be seen in Britain	1

Level 3 Reading Comprehension Test

Maximum mark is **23**

Spelling Test

- For each word there is one mark for writing the initial letter (or, in some cases, pair of letters) correctly and one mark for the correct spelling of the whole word. Each answer will therefore receive a mark of 0, 1 or 2.
- Do not deduct any marks for the incorrect use of capital and lower case letters.
- Ignore any spaces between letters. Marks can be awarded provided all the letters are present and in the correct order.

MARKET DAY – PART 1

Question	Answer	Mark (initial letter(s))	Mark (whole word)
Practice	cup	—	—
1	coat	1 (**c**)	1
2	balloons	1 (**b**)	1
3	glass	1 (**gl**)	1
4	ball	1 (**b**)	1
5	clock	1 (**cl**)	1
6	dress	1 (**dr**)	1
7	clown	1 (**cl**)	1
8	seat	1 (**s**)	1
9	bag	1 (**b**)	1
10	train	1 (**tr**)	1

MARKET DAY – PART 2

Question	Answer	Mark (initial letter(s))	Mark (whole word)
Practice	on	—	—
1	went	1 (**w**)	1
2	buy	1 (**b**)	1
3	party	1 (**p**)	1
4	baker	1 (**b**)	1
5	cake	1 (**c**)	1
6	little	1 (**l**)	1
7	paper	1 (**p**)	1
8	game	1 (**g**)	1
9	blue	1 (**bl**)	1
10	picked	1 (**p**)	1
11	food	1 (**f**)	1
12	cheese	1 (**ch**)	1
13	apples	1 (**a**)	1
14	fruit	1 (**fr**)	1
15	vegetables	1 (**v**)	1
16	help	1 (**h**)	1
17	home	1 (**h**)	1
18	sandwich	1 (**s**)	1
19	drink	1 (**dr**)	1
20	crisps	1 (**cr**)	1

Spelling Test
Maximum mark is **60**

Dictation passage

Below is the full version of the story that appears in Part 2 of the Spelling Test (pages 48 and 49). As explained on page 44, you should read the story aloud to your child, pausing at each of the words in bold print.

It is my birthday **on** Saturday. Today I **went** with my mum to the market to **buy** some things we needed for my **party**

The **baker** had ready the **cake** my mum had ordered. It looked lovely. Then we bought some **little** toys. I am going to wrap these toys up in lots of **paper** for a 'pass the parcel' **game**

Mum then bought me some new shoes. First I tried on a **blue** pair, but they were too tight. Then I tried on a red pair. They were very comfortable and Mum and I **picked** these.

Mum then bought some **food**. She bought **cheese** and eggs from the dairy counter. She also bought oranges and **apples** from the **fruit** and **vegetables** stall.

Then we met Grandad. He was going to **help** us carry everything back **home**. First we all went to the café. Mum and Grandad had some coffee and shared a **sandwich**. I had an orange **drink** and a packet of **crisps**

Marking scheme

The **Levels of Achievement** grading system that is used in the National Tests is explained on page v. Level 2 is the level most 7 year olds are expected to reach. Level 3 means the child's performance is above the expected level for most children of this age. Level 1 means the child is working towards the level of performance expected at this age.

Reading Comprehension Tests

Level 2

Number of marks	Level
0–7 (inclusive)	Level 2 not achieved
8–18 (inclusive)	Level 2C achieved
19–23 (inclusive)	Level 2B achieved
24–29 (inclusive)	Level 2A achieved

Level 3

Number of marks	Level
0–13 (inclusive)	Level 3 not achieved
14–23 (inclusive)	Level 3 achieved

Spelling Test

Number of marks	Level
0–16 (inclusive)	Level 1 not achieved
17–31 (inclusive)	Level 1 achieved
32–52 (inclusive)	Level 2 achieved
53–60 (inclusive)	Level 3 achieved

A mark in the Level 2A range indicates that your child is ready to attempt the Level 3 Reading Comprehension Test.

LONGMAN TEST PRACTICE KITS

KEY STAGE 1

English
National Tests

Considerable importance is placed upon the National Tests (formerly known as SATs) that face children at the end of year 2, and, as a parent, you'll want to give your child the best possible chance of success.

Longman Test Practice Kits explain exactly what the tests are all about, and, by providing lots of practice and helpful hints, will help you and your child prepare as thoroughly as possible, assuring them of the best result.

Covering the major topic areas for English at Key Stage 1, this book includes:

- an explanation of what the test actually consists of – and how it will be assessed
- examples of past test paper questions – offering your child lots of practice, right up to the tests themselves
- solutions to questions – with advice for parents on what to look for in an answer
- a straightforward mark assessment system – see how your child progresses, and assess their likely National Curriculum level.

✔ **National Tests explained**

✔ **Test questions – with answers**

✔ **Straightforward marking scheme – assess your child's likely National Curriculum level**

The Author:

Alan Gardiner is a teacher and English Examiner. He is the author of *Longman Test Practice Kits: Key Stage 2 English* and *Key Stage 3 English* and *Longman Homework Handbooks: Key Stage 3 English*.

Longman Test Practice Kits - giving your child the best chance

Visit our web site at awl-he.com/studyguides

£3.99 net
ISBN 0-582-41489-X

9 780582 414891 >